Singalonga Christmas!

Wise Publications
London/New York/Paris/Sydney

NON-STOP MUSIC!

Exclusive Distributors:
Music Sales Limited
8/9 Frith Street, London W1V 5TZ, England.
Music Sales Pty Limited
120 Rothschild Avenue,
Rosebery, NSW 2018, Australia.

This book © Copyright 1992 by
Wise Publications
Order No.AM89750
ISBN 0-7119-3072-4

Book design by Pearce Marchbank Studio
Computer origination by Adam Hay
Compiled by Peter Evans and Peter Lavender
Music arranged by Peter Lavender
Music processed by Musicprint
Printed in the United Kingdom by
J.B. Offset Printers (Marks Tey) Limited,
Marks Tey, Essex.

Music Sales' complete catalogue lists thousands of titles and is free from your local music shop, or direct from Music Sales Limited. Please send a cheque/postal order for £1.75 for postage to: Music Sales, Newmarket Road, Bury St. Edmunds, Suffolk IP33 3YB.

Your Guarantee of Quality
As publishers, we strive to produce every book to the highest commercial standards.
The music has been freshly engraved and the book has been carefully designed to minimise awkward page turns and to make playing from it a real pleasure.
Particular care has been given to specifying acid-free, neutral-sized paper which has not been chlorine bleached but produced with special regard for the environment. Throughout, the printing and binding have been planned to ensure a sturdy, attractive publication which should give years of enjoyment.
If your copy fails to meet our high standards, please inform us and we will gladly replace it.

Musical tones are represented by <u>notes</u> written on five horizontal lines called the <u>stave</u>. The position of each note on the stave denotes its <u>pitch</u>.

Notes too high or too low to be placed within the stave appear on short lines above or below it, called <u>leger lines.</u>

The specific pitch of notes is indicated by letter-names, using the first 7 letters of the alphabet.

A <u>clef</u> sign appearing at the beginning of the staff fixes the pitch or letter-name of one particular note, from which all other notes are related and named in the musical alphabet sequence.

The G Clef (Treble Clef) fixes G on the 2nd line:

The F Clef (Bass Clef) fixes F on the 4th line:

The following illustration shows many of the notes on a keyboard (including sharps and flats) with their letter-names in the bass and treble clefs.

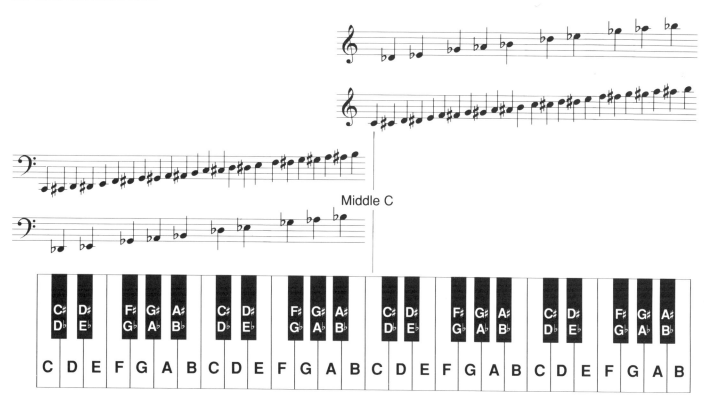

Middle C

<u>Sharps</u> and <u>flats</u> are placed before notes to raise or lower the pitch by a half-tone (semitone). A sharp ♯ raises the note a semitone. A flat ♭ lowers the note a semitone. The <u>natural</u> ♮ cancels the sharp or flat, restoring the note to original pitch.

A key signature at the beginning of each stave indicates which notes are to be played as sharps or flats, irrespective of their position in or around the stave. These are the most frequently used key signatures:

C Major	G Major	F Major	D Major	B♭ Major	A Major	E♭ Major
A Minor	E Minor	D Minor	B Minor	G Minor	F♯ Minor	C Minor

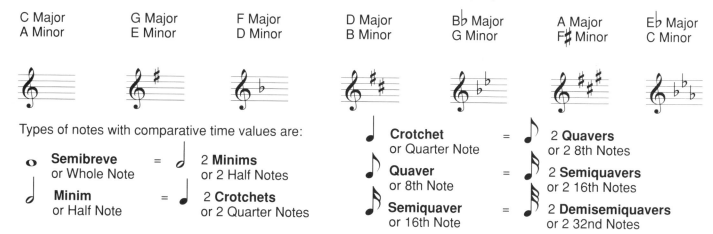

Types of notes with comparative time values are:

𝅝 **Semibreve** = 𝅗𝅥 2 **Minims**
or Whole Note   or 2 Half Notes

𝅗𝅥 **Minim** = 𝅘𝅥 2 **Crotchets**
or Half Note   or 2 Quarter Notes

𝅘𝅥 **Crotchet** = 𝅘𝅥𝅮 2 **Quavers**
or Quarter Note   or 2 8th Notes

𝅘𝅥𝅮 **Quaver** = 𝅘𝅥𝅯 2 **Semiquavers**
or 8th Note   or 2 16th Notes

𝅘𝅥𝅯 **Semiquaver** = 𝅘𝅥𝅰 2 **Demisemiquavers**
or 16th Note   or 2 32nd Notes

Eighth notes and notes of shorter duration in time can be joined together by cross bars called beams.

Music is divided by vertical lines called **Bars** (or bar lines) into portions called **Measures**. The total time value in each measure is shown at the beginning of the music by a time signature consisting of an upper and lower number. The upper indicates the number of counts (beats) within each measure; the lower number explains the time value of each count.

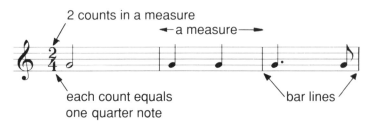

2 counts in a measure
← a measure →
each count equals one quarter note
bar lines

Common time signatures: $\frac{2}{4}$ $\frac{3}{4}$ $\frac{4}{4}$ $\frac{3}{8}$ $\frac{6}{8}$ $\frac{9}{8}$ $\frac{12}{8}$

Special time signatures: $\mathbf{C} = \frac{4}{4}$ $\mathbf{\mathcal{C}} = \frac{2}{2}$ (cut time, called **alla breve**)

Rests (periods of silence) have time values equal to notes of the same name.

Semibreve Rest

Minim Rest

Crotchet Rest

Quaver Rest

Semiquaver Rest

Demisemiquaver Rest

A double bar shows the end of a composition or portion of it.

A section of music to be played twice is indicated as follows:

repeat the music in between.

Sometimes a repeated passage has a different closing when played the second time. In this instance first and second endings are used:

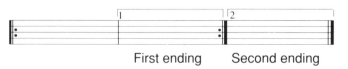

First ending   Second ending

Common musical terms and abbreviations:

D.C. (Da Capo): from the beginning.

D.S. (Dal Segno): from the sign %.

Coda: meaning 'tail', a separated section of music that forms the end of an arrangement, and is represented by the sign ⊕.

D.C. al Coda, and D.S. al Coda: return as indicated and play up to the point marked al Coda, then skip to the Coda section.

Fine: the end.

D.C. al Fine, or D.S. al Fine: return as indicated and play to Fine.

Fingered Chords

The recurring patterns of equally spaced notes (intervals) in Augmented and Diminished chords result in groups of chord symbols having the same note structure:

Augmented Chords

C aug = E aug = G♯aug = A♭aug =

C♯aug = D♭aug = Faug = Aaug =

Daug = F♯aug = G♭aug = A♯aug = B♭aug =

D♯aug = E♭aug = G aug = B aug =

Diminished Chords

C dim = D♯dim = E♭dim = F♯dim = G♭dim = A dim =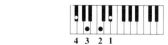

C♯dim = D♭dim = E dim = G dim = A♯dim = B♭dim =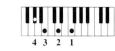

D dim = F dim = G♯dim = A♭dim = B dim =

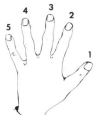

Master Chord Chart

	Major	Minor	Seventh	Minor Seventh
C	5 2 1	5 2 1	5 3 2 1	5 3 2 1
C# Db	4 2 1	4 2 1	4 3 2 1	4 3 2 1
D	5 3 1	5 2 1	5 3 2 1	5 3 2 1
Eb	5 3 1	5 3 1	5 4 2 1	5 3 2 1
E	4 3 1	5 3 1	4 3 2 1	5 4 2 1
F	5 3 1	5 3 1	5 3 2 1	5 3 2 1
F# Gb	4 2 1	4 2 1	5 3 2 1	5 3 2 1
G	5 3 1	5 3 1	5 3 2 1	5 3 2 1
Ab	4 2 1	4 2 1	5 4 2 1	5 4 2 1
A	4 2 1	4 2 1	5 4 2 1	5 4 2 1
Bb	4 2 1	4 2 1	5 4 2 1	5 4 2 1
B	4 2 1	4 2 1	4 3 2 1	4 3 2 1

Medley 1

Registration: Trumpet or Saxophone
Rhythm: Swing
Tempo: Medium Fast

SNOWY WHITE SNOW
AND JINGLE BELLS

Snow - y White Snow And
Ev - 'ry - one's gay, and

Jin - gle Bells, Oh what a hap - py sea - son, Snow - y White Snow And
wish you well, They have a sim - ple rea - son, Lit - tle red rob - bins

Jin - gle Bells, Ech - o - ing all day long. Fai - ry lights and
in the dell, Sing - ing a hap - py song.

star - ry nights, You can have your wish. Can - dle glow and

mis - tle - toe, It's time to steal a kiss! Snow - y White Snow And

Jin - gle Bells, Join in the ca - rol sing - ing, Wish - ing to you and

THE WHITE WORLD OF WINTER

ev - er a mo - ment you are freez - in', Just a lit - tle

squeez - in', Could be might - y pleas - in'! In this

won - der - ful White World Of Win - ter, _____ I'm fall - in'

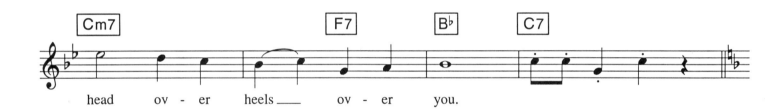

head ov - er heels ___ ov - er you.

HERE COMES SANTA CLAUS

Here Comes San - ta Claus! Here Comes San - ta Claus! Right down San - ta Claus

Lane! High in the sky you will see his rein - deer are pull - ing on the

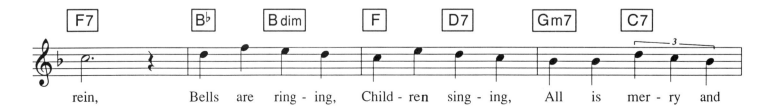

rein, Bells are ring - ing, Chil - dren sing - ing, All is mer - ry and

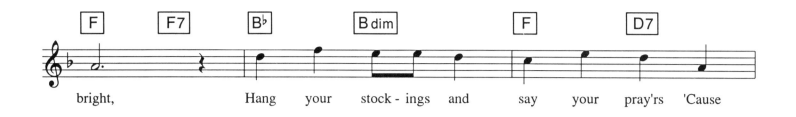

bright, Hang your stock - ings and say your pray'rs 'Cause

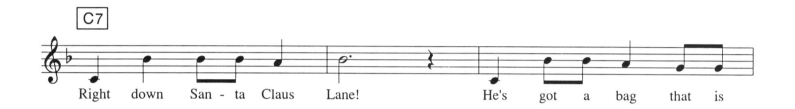

San - ta Claus comes to - night! Here Comes San - ta Claus! Here Comes San - ta Claus!

Right down San - ta Claus Lane! He's got a bag that is

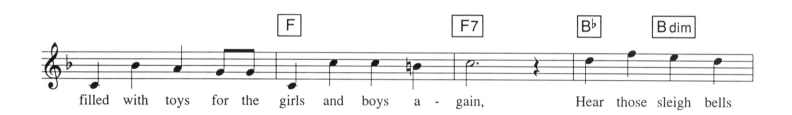

filled with toys for the girls and boys a - gain, Hear those sleigh bells

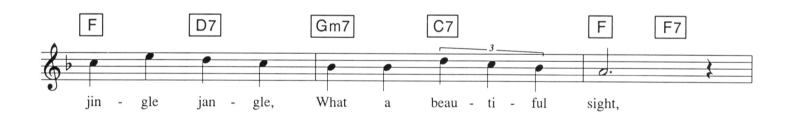

jin - gle jan - gle, What a beau - ti - ful sight,

Jump in bed, Co - ver up your head, 'Cause San - ta Claus comes to - night!

I'M GOING HOME FOR CHRISTMAS

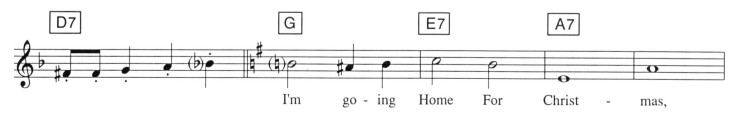

I'm go - ing Home For Christ - mas,

9

Do you won - der why I'm glad?_____ I've got a

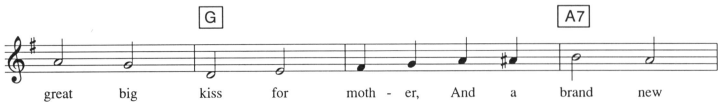

great big kiss for moth - er, And a brand new

pipe for dad._____ There's no place like home for

Christ - mas, When you're with the ones you love;_____

___ Jin - gle bells, Jin - gle bells, Jin - gle all the

way! I'm Go - ing Home For Christ - mas to - day,_____ I'm Go - ing

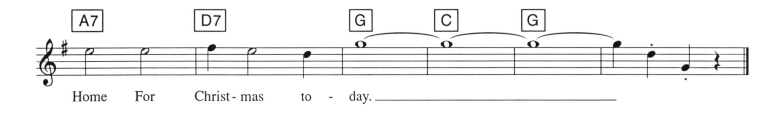

Home For Christ - mas to - day._____

Registration: Flute or Strings
Rhythm: Waltz
Tempo: Medium Fast

WE THREE KINGS

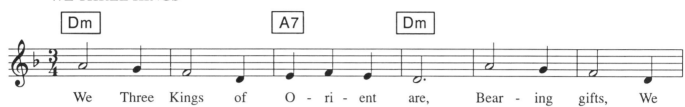

We Three Kings of O - ri - ent are, Bear - ing gifts, We

tra - verse a - far, Field and foun - tain, Moor and moun - tain,

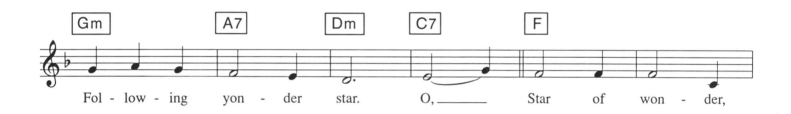

Fol - low - ing yon - der star. O, _____ Star of won - der,

Star of night, Star with roy - al beau - ty bright,

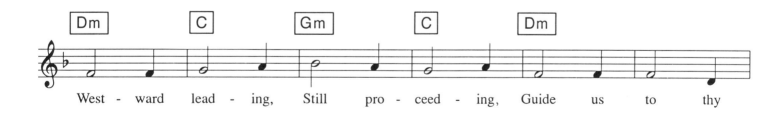

West - ward lead - ing, Still pro - ceed - ing, Guide us to thy

WE WISH YOU A MERRY CHRISTMAS

per - fect light. We Wish You A Mer - ry Christ - mas, We

Wish You A Mer-ry Christ-mas, We Wish You A Mer-ry Christ-mas, And a

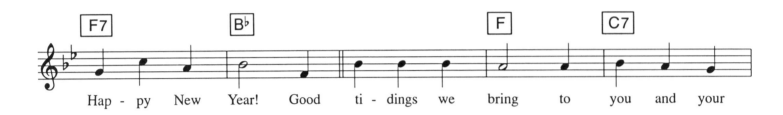

Hap-py New Year! Good ti-dings we bring to you and your

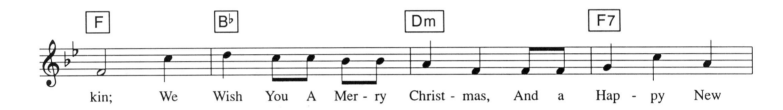

kin; We Wish You A Mer-ry Christ-mas, And a Hap-py New

THE HOLLY AND THE IVY

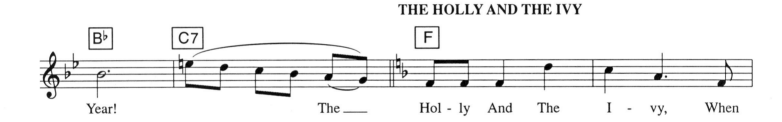

Year! The ___ Hol-ly And The I - vy, When

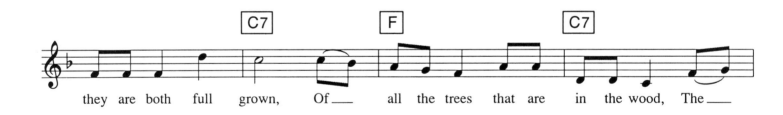

they are both full grown, Of ___ all the trees that are in the wood, The ___

hol-ly wears the crown. The ris-ing of the sun, ___ And the

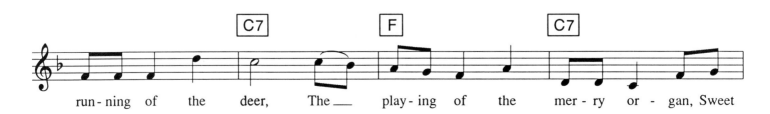

run-ning of the deer, The ___ play-ing of the mer-ry or - gan, Sweet

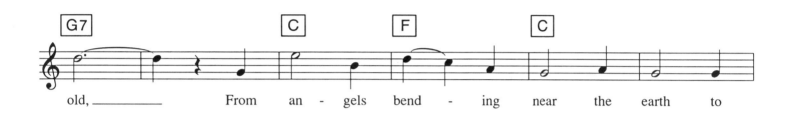

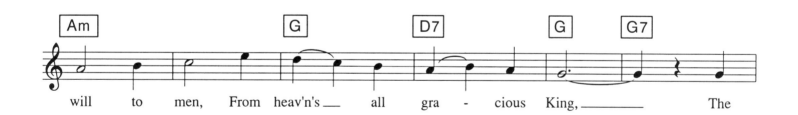

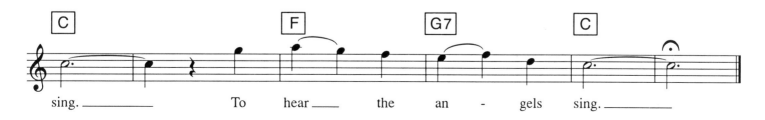

Medley 3

Registration: Flute or Human Chorus
Rhythm: Beguine
Tempo: Medium

ALL THROUGH THE NIGHT

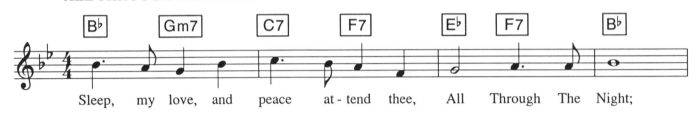

Sleep, my love, and peace at - tend thee, All Through The Night;

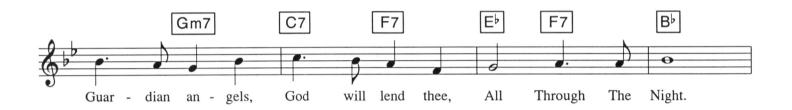

Guar - dian an - gels, God will lend thee, All Through The Night.

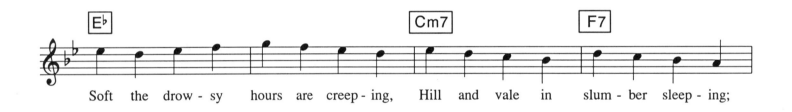

Soft the drow - sy hours are creep - ing, Hill and vale in slum - ber sleep - ing;

Love a - lone his watch is keep - ing, All Through The Night.

IN THE BLEAK MIDWINTER

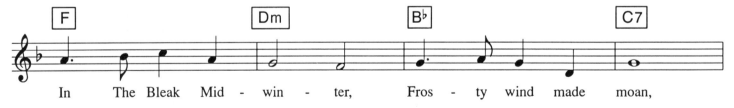

In The Bleak Mid - win - ter, Fros - ty wind made moan,

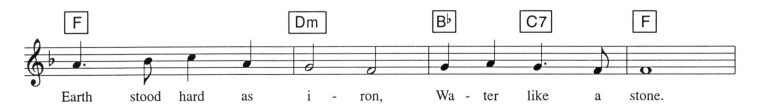

Earth stood hard as i - ron, Wa - ter like a stone.

14

Snow had fall - en, Snow on snow, Snow _____ on _____ snow,

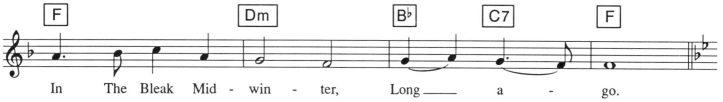

In The Bleak Mid - win - ter, Long _____ a - go.

ANGELS WE HAVE HEARD ON HIGH

An - gels We Have Heard On High, Sweet - ly sing - ing o'er the plains,

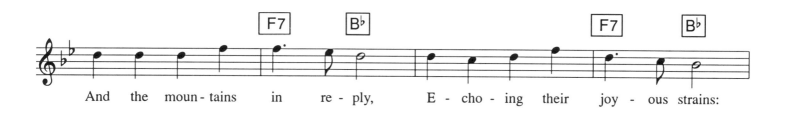

And the moun - tains in re - ply, E - cho - ing their joy - ous strains:

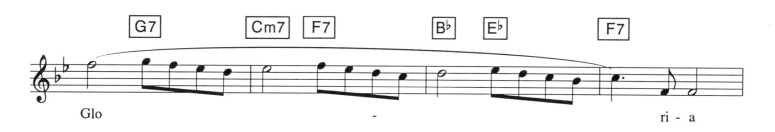

Glo - ri - a

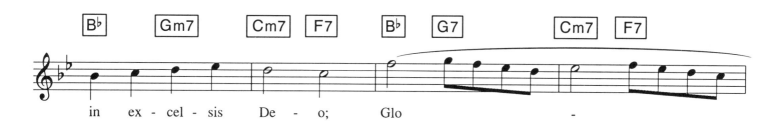

in ex - cel - sis De - o; Glo -

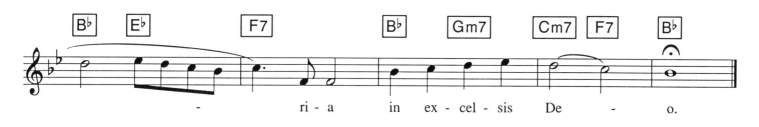

- ri - a in ex - cel - sis De - o.

Registration: Pop Organ or Rock Guitar
Rhythm: Rock
Tempo: Medium

JINGLE BELL ROCK

Jin - gle bell, Jin - gle bell, Jin - gle Bell Rock, — Jin - gle bell swing and

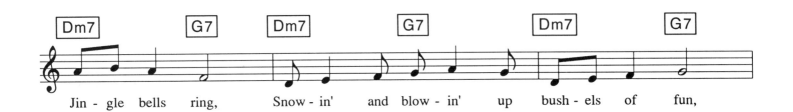

Jin - gle bells ring, Snow - in' and blow - in' up bush - els of fun,

Now the Jin - gle hop has be - gun. — Jin - gle bell, Jin - gle bell,

Jin - gle Bell Rock, — Jin - gle bells chime in jin - gle bell time,

Dan - cin' and pran - cin' in Jin - gle Bell Square, In the fros - ty air. —

— What a bright — time, — It's the right — time — to

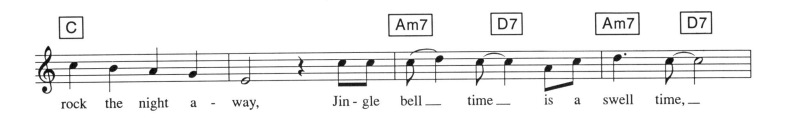

rock the night a-way, Jin-gle bell _ time _ is a swell time, _

To go gli-din' in a one-horse sleigh! _ Gid-dy-ap, Jin-gle horse,

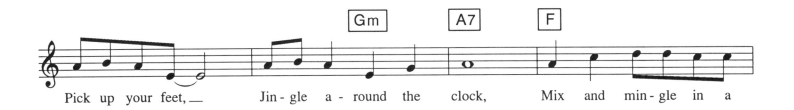

Pick up your feet, _ Jin-gle a-round the clock, Mix and min-gle in a

jin-gl-in' beat, _ That's the Jin-gle Bell Rock. When the

I WISH IT COULD BE CHRISTMAS EVERY DAY

snow-man brings the snow, _ Oh well he just might like to know, _

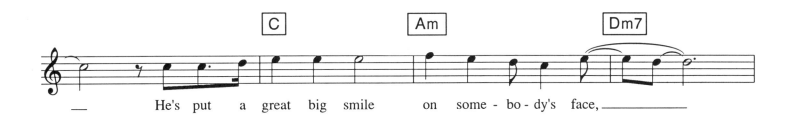

_ He's put a great big smile on some-bo-dy's face, _

If you jump in-to your bed, _ Quick-ly cov-er up _ your head, _

Don't you lock the doors, __ You know that sweet San - ta Claus is on the

way. _____ Oh well I Wish It Could Be Christ - mas __ Ev - 'ry Day, __

When the kids start sing - ing and the

band be - gins __ to play; _____ Oh __ I Wish It Could Be Christ -

- mas Ev - 'ry Day, _____ So let the bells ring out for

MERRY CHRISTMAS EVERYBODY

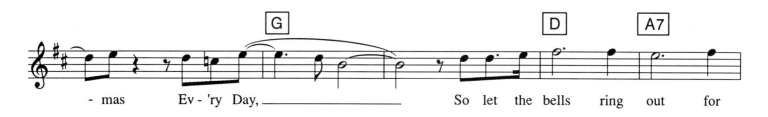

Christ - mas. _____ Are you hang - ing up __ a stock - ing on __ your wall? __

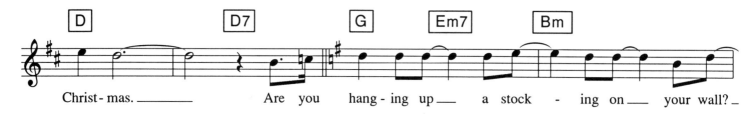

__ It's the time that ev - 'ry San - ta has __ a ball, __

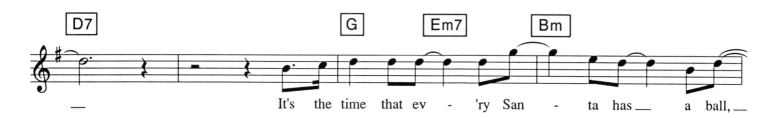

- ing on ___ your wall? ___ Are you hop - ing that ___ the snow ___

___ will start ___ to fall? ___ Do you

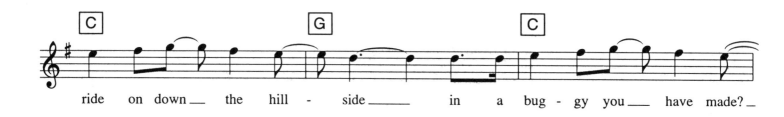

ride on down ___ the hill - side ___ in a bug - gy you ___ have made? ___

___ When you land up - on ___ your head ___ then you ___ bin slayed!

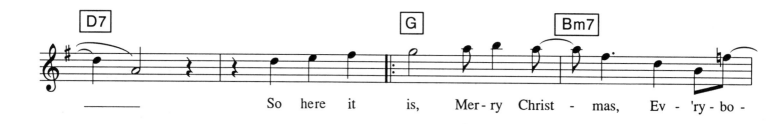

___ So here it is, Mer - ry Christ - mas, Ev - 'ry - bo -

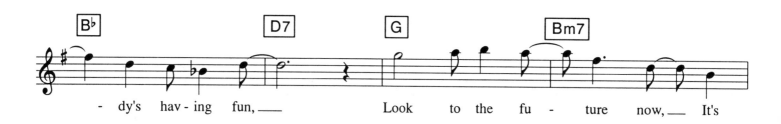

- dy's hav - ing fun, ___ Look to the fu - ture now, ___ It's

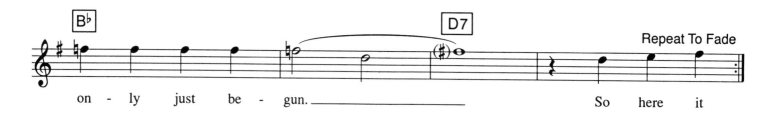

on - ly just be - gun. ___ So here it

20

Registration: Horn or Saxophone
Rhythm: Waltz
Tempo: Medium

WHAT CHILD IS THIS

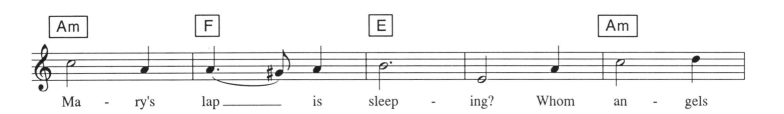

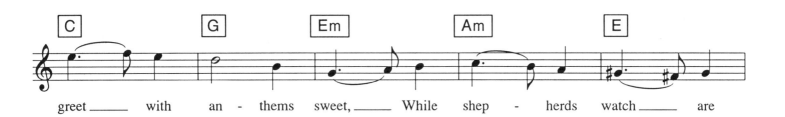

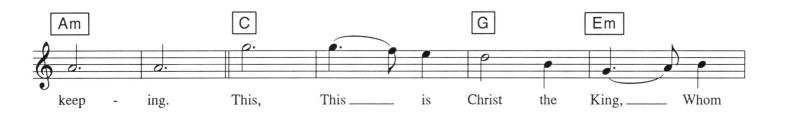

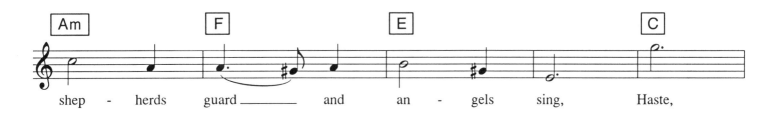

Son ___ of Ma - ry. A - way In A ___ Man - ger, No ___

crib for a bed, The ___ lit - tle Lord Je - sus laid ___

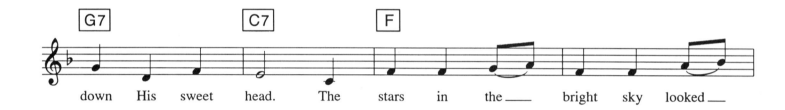

down His sweet head. The stars in the ___ bright sky looked ___

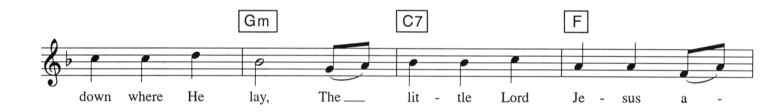

down where He lay, The ___ lit - tle Lord Je - sus a -

THE FIRST NOWELL

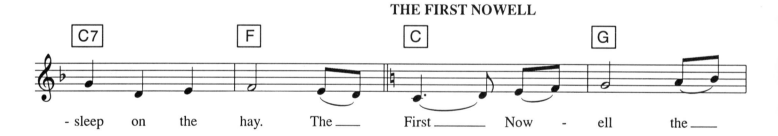

- sleep on the hay. The ___ First ___ Now - ell the ___

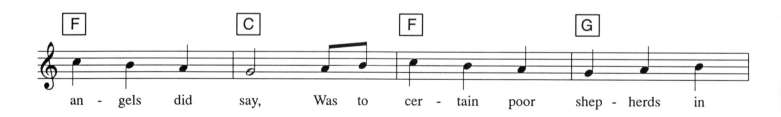

an - gels did say, Was to cer - tain poor shep - herds in

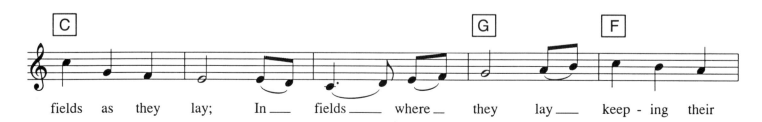

fields as they lay; In ___ fields ___ where ___ they lay ___ keep - ing their

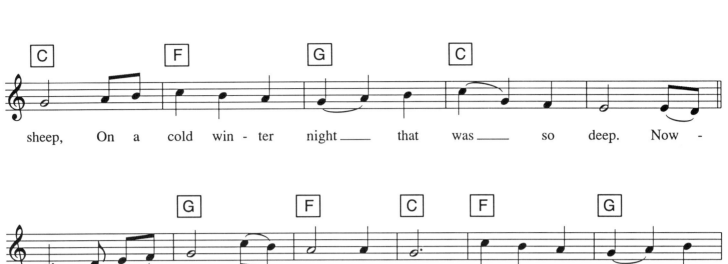

sheep, On a cold win-ter night ___ that was ___ so deep. Now -

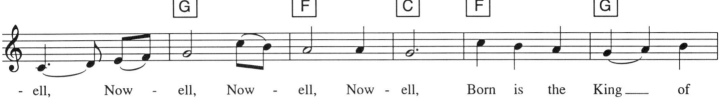

- ell, Now - ell, Now - ell, Now - ell, Born is the King ___ of

O CHRISTMAS TREE

Is - ra - el. O Christ-mas Tree, O Christ-mas Tree, You

stand in ver-dant beau-ty! O Christ-mas Tree, O Christ-mas Tree, You

stand in ver-dant beau-ty! Your boughs are green in sum-mer's glow, And

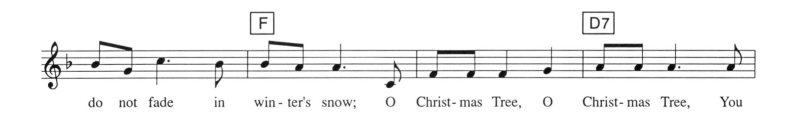

do not fade in win-ter's snow; O Christ-mas Tree, O Christ-mas Tree, You

stand in ver-dant beau-ty! You stand in ver-dant beau-ty! ___

Medley 6

Registration: Synth Brass or Celesta
Rhythm: Christmas Rock or Disco
Tempo: Medium

Optional Intro (Repeat ad lib.) **O COME ALL YE FAITHFUL**

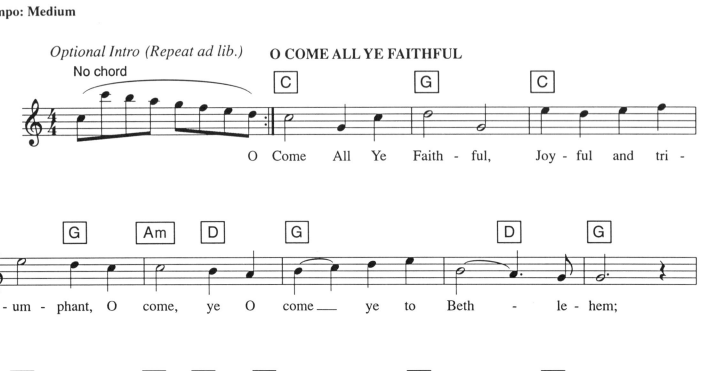

O Come All Ye Faith - ful, Joy - ful and tri - um - phant, O come, ye O come ___ ye to Beth - le - hem;

Come and be - hold Him, born the King of An - gels, O come let us a - dore Him, O come let us a - dore Him, O come let us a - dore Him, ___

WHILE SHEPHERDS WATCHED THEIR FLOCKS

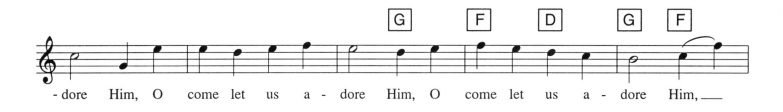

Christ ___ the Lord. While Shep - herds Watched Their Flocks by night, All

seat - ed on the ground, The An - gel of the Lord came down, And

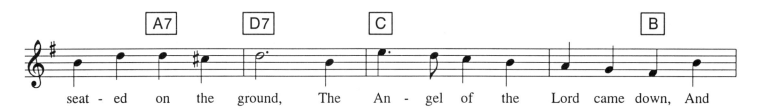

HARK THE HERALD
ANGELS SING

DING DONG MERRILY ON HIGH

Registration: Saxophone or Strings

Rhythm: Waltz

Tempo: Medium

SANTO NATALE

No chord | F7 | B♭ | F7 | E♭

Instrumental San - to Na - ta - le, San - to Na -

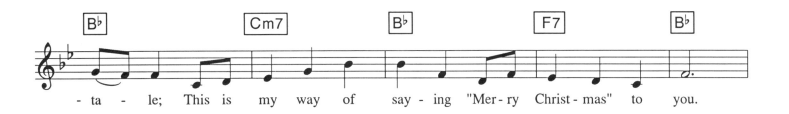

B♭ | Cm7 | B♭ | F7 | B♭

-ta - le; This is my way of say - ing "Mer - ry Christ - mas" to you.

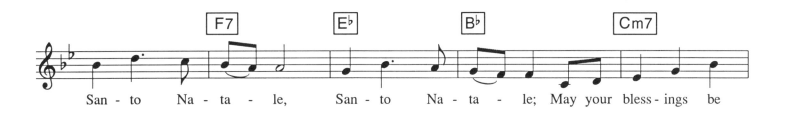

F7 | E♭ | B♭ | Cm7

San - to Na - ta - le, San - to Na - ta - le; May your bless - ings be

B♭ | F7 | B♭ | E♭ | B♭

man - y and your trou - bles be few. To those I love who are so dear, Tho' we are

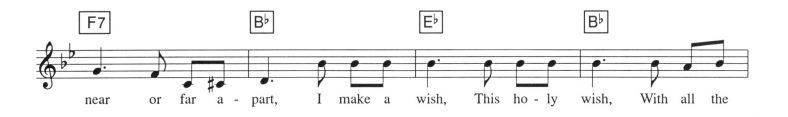

F7 | B♭ | E♭ | B♭

near or far a - part, I make a wish, This ho - ly wish, With all the

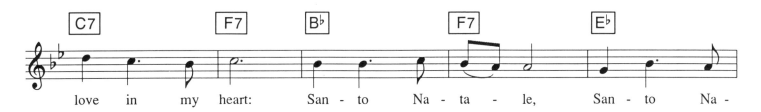

C7 | F7 | B♭ | F7 | E♭

love in my heart: San - to Na - ta - le, San - to Na -

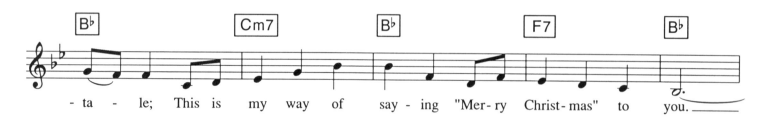
-ta - le; This is my way of say-ing "Mer-ry Christ-mas" to you.

THE VERY FIRST CHRISTMAS OF ALL

One night when the world was a - sleep, _____ While

shep-herds were watch-ing their sheep, _____ They gazed from a - far at a

star they saw, Then fol-lowed that star to a sta - ble door; A

child in a man - ger they found, _____ With gifts made of gold on the

ground, _____ And so it be - gan, In that hum - ble stall, The

SILENT NIGHT

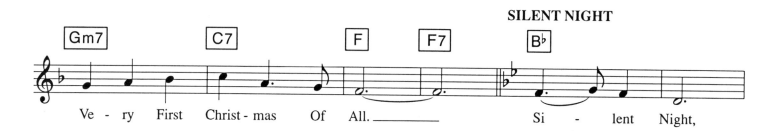
Ve - ry First Christ-mas Of All. _____ Si - lent Night,

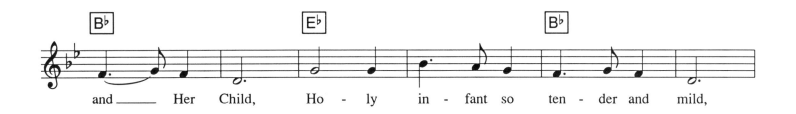

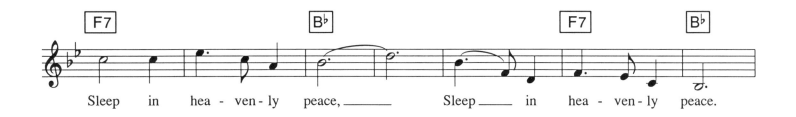

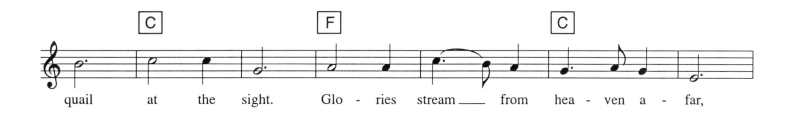

Registration: Horn or Human Chorus (+ Reverb)

Rhythm: Beguine

Tempo: Medium

ONCE IN ROYAL DAVID'S CITY

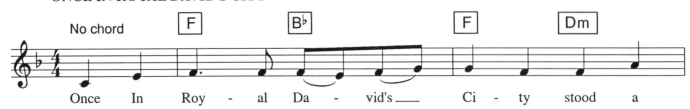

Once In Roy - al Da - vid's ___ Ci - ty stood a

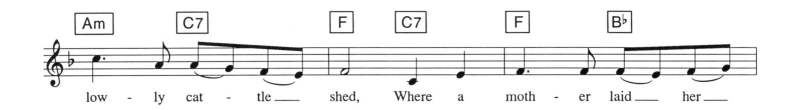

low - ly cat - tle ___ shed, Where a moth - er laid ___ her ___

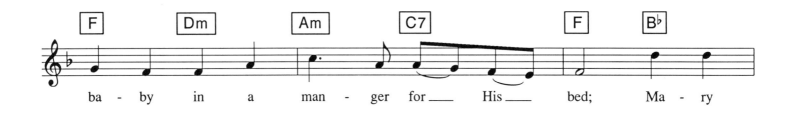

ba - by in a man - ger for ___ His ___ bed; Ma - ry

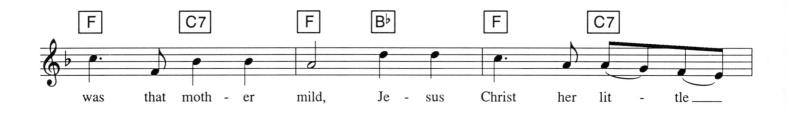

was that moth - er mild, Je - sus Christ her lit - tle ___

MARY'S BOY CHILD

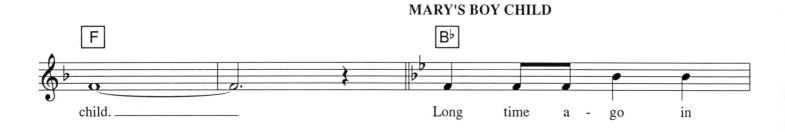

child. ___ Long time a - go in

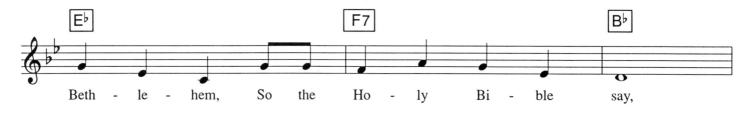

Beth - le - hem, So the Ho - ly Bi - ble say,

30

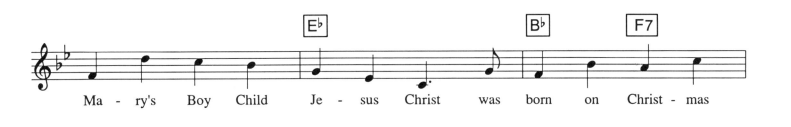

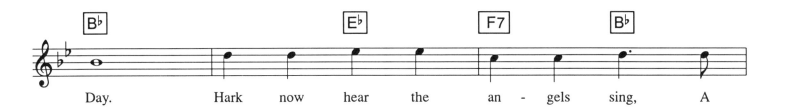

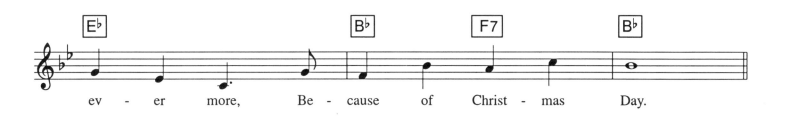

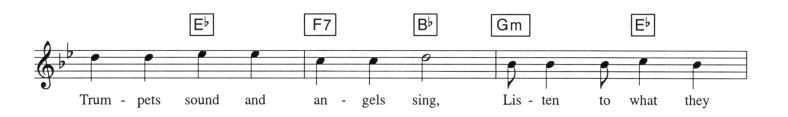

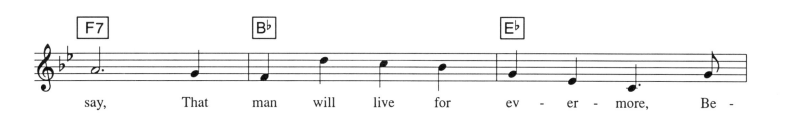

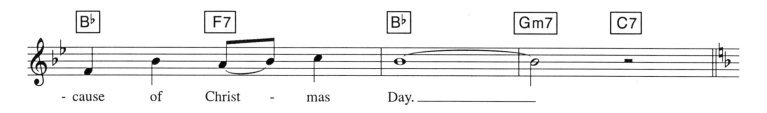

THE LITTLE DRUMMER BOY

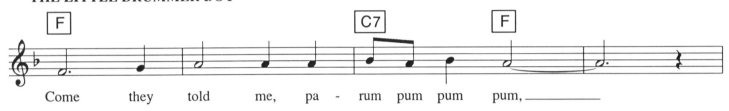

Come they told me, pa - rum pum pum pum, _____

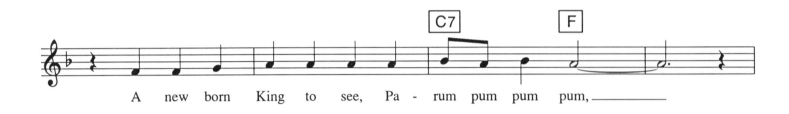

A new born King to see, Pa - rum pum pum pum, _____

Our fin - est gifts we bring, Pa - rum pum pum pum, _____

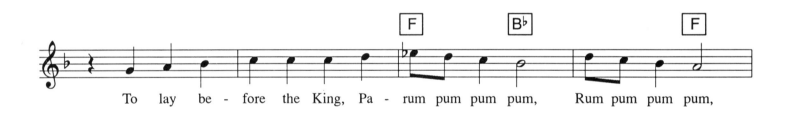

To lay be - fore the King, Pa - rum pum pum pum, Rum pum pum pum,

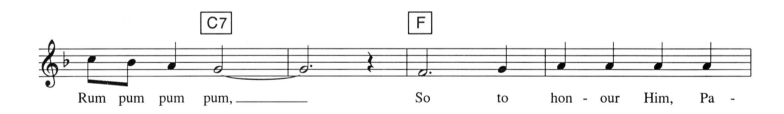

Rum pum pum pum, _____ So to hon - our Him, Pa -

- rum pum pum pum, _____ When ___ we come. _____

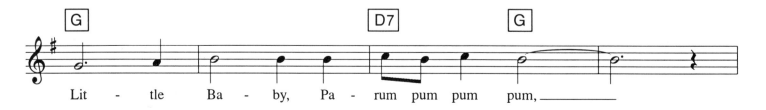

Lit - tle Ba - by, Pa - rum pum pum pum, _____

I am a poor boy too, Pa - rum pum pum pum, _____

I have no gift to bring, Pa - rum pum pum pum, _____

That's fit to give our King, Pa - rum pum pum pum,

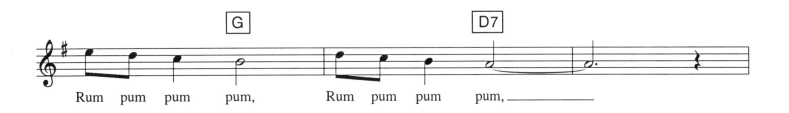

Rum pum pum pum, Rum pum pum pum, _____

So I'll play for you, Pa - rum pum pum pum, _____

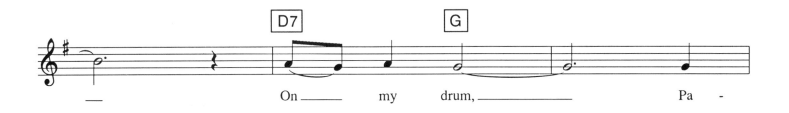

_ On ___ my drum, _____ Pa -

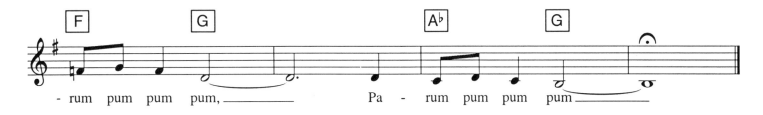

- rum pum pum pum, _____ Pa - rum pum pum pum _____

Medley 9

Registration: Trombone or Pipe Organ (+ Reverb)
Rhythm: Swing
Tempo: Medium Fast

GOD REST YOU MERRY GENTLEMEN

God Rest You Mer - ry Gen - tle - men, Let noth - ing you dis - may, Re -

- mem - ber Christ our sa - viour was born on Christ - mas Day, To

save poor souls from Sa - tan's power which had long time gone a - stray, And it's

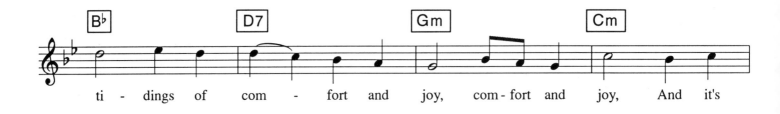

ti - dings of com - fort and joy, com - fort and joy, And it's

GOOD KING WENCESLAS

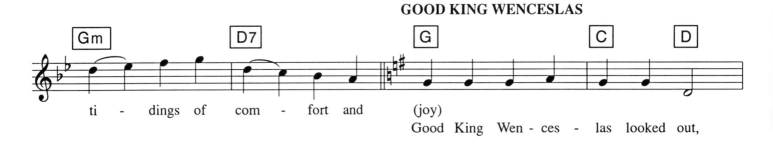

ti - dings of com - fort and (joy)
Good King Wen - ces - las looked out,

On the feast of Ste - phen, When the snow lay round a - bout,

34

SANTA CLAUS IS COMIN' TO TOWN

35

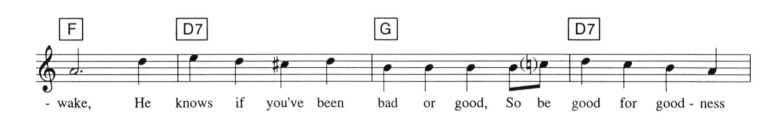

- wake, He knows if you've been bad or good, So be good for good - ness

sake, Oh! You bet - ter watch out, You bet - ter not cry, Bet - ter not pout, I'm

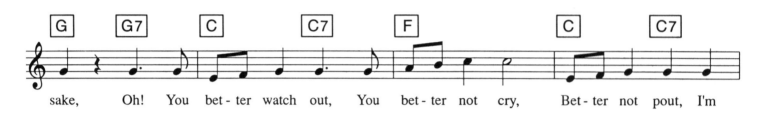

tell - ing you why: San - ta Claus Is Com - in' To Town. _____

JINGLE BELLS

Jin - gle Bells, Jin - gle Bells, Jin - gle all the way, Oh what fun it

is to ride in a one - horse o - pen sleigh. Jin - gle Bells, Jin - gle Bells,

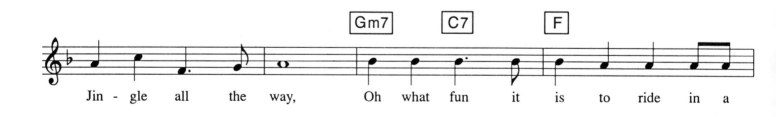

Jin - gle all the way, Oh what fun it is to ride in a

one - horse o - pen sleigh. Dash - ing thro' the snow, In a

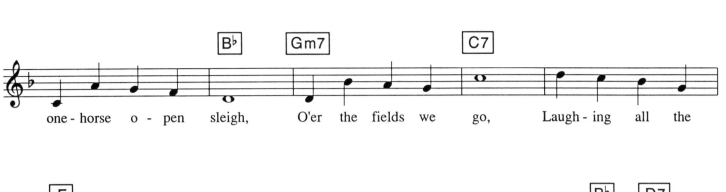

one - horse o - pen sleigh, O'er the fields we go, Laugh - ing all the

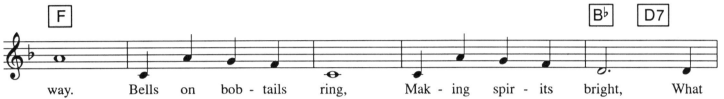

way. Bells on bob - tails ring, Mak - ing spir - its bright, What

fun it is to ride and sing a sleigh - ing song to - night!

Jin - gle Bells, Jin - gle Bells, Jin - gle all the way, Oh what fun it

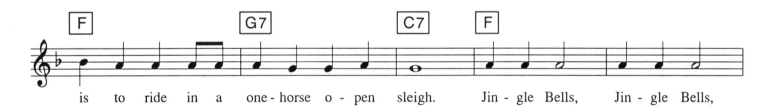

is to ride in a one - horse o - pen sleigh. Jin - gle Bells, Jin - gle Bells,

Jin - gle all the way, Oh what fun it is to ride in a

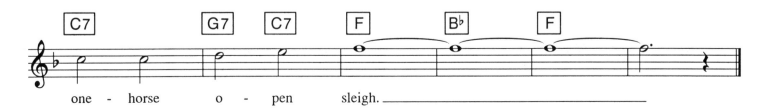

one - horse o - pen sleigh.

Medley 10

Registration: Vibraphone or Piano
Rhythm: Swing
Tempo: Medium

A MARSHMALLOW WORLD

No chord   C

It's   A   Marsh - mal - low World   in   the   win - ter, _____   When   the

G7   Dm7   G7

snow   comes   to   co - ver   the   ground,   It's   the   time   for   play, ____   It's   a

C   Am7   D7   G7

whipped   cream   day, ____   I   wait   for   it   the   whole   year   'round.   Those   are

C

Marsh - mal - low   clouds   be - ing   friend - ly, _____   In   the   arms   of   the   e - ver - green

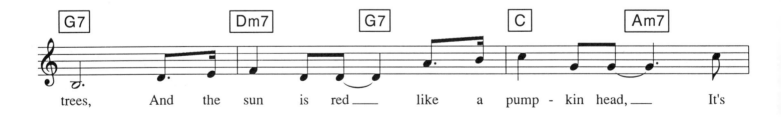

G7   Dm7   G7   C   Am7

trees,   And   the   sun   is   red ____   like   a   pump - kin   head, ____   It's

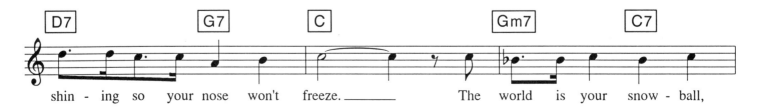

D7   G7   C   Gm7   C7

shin - ing   so   your   nose   won't   freeze. _____   The   world   is   your   snow - ball,

See how it grows, That's how it goes, When - e - ver it snows, The

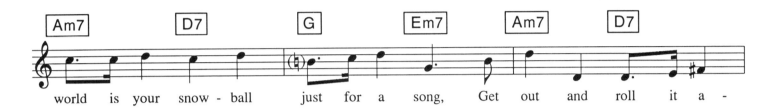

world is your snow - ball just for a song, Get out and roll it a -

- long! ____ It's a yum yum - my world made for sweet-hearts, ____ Take a

walk with your fa - vour - ite girl, It's a su - gar date, ___ What if

spring is late, ___ In win - ter it's A Marsh - mal - low World.

I SAW MOMMY KISSING SANTA CLAUS

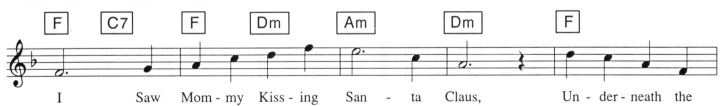

I Saw Mom - my Kiss - ing San - ta Claus, Un - der - neath the

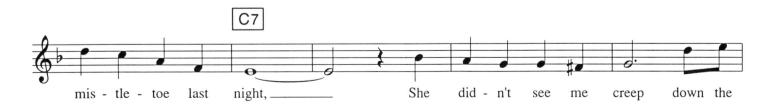

mis - tle - toe last night, _____ She did - n't see me creep down the

39

stairs to have a peep, She thought that I was tucked up in my

bed - room fast a - sleep. Then I saw mom - my tick - le San - ta

Claus, Un - der - neath his beard so snow - y white, _____

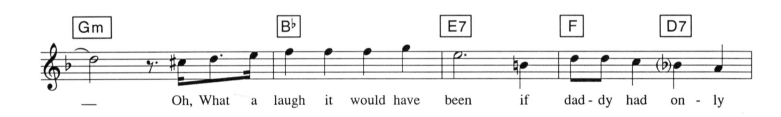

_____ Oh, What a laugh it would have been if dad - dy had on - ly

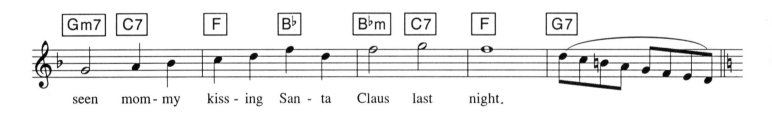

seen mom - my kiss - ing San - ta Claus last night.

HAVE YOURSELF A MERRY LITTLE CHRISTMAS

Have Your - self A Mer - ry Lit - tle Christ - mas, Let your heart be light,

From now on our trou - bles will be out of sight, _____

Medley 11

Registration: Strings or Woodwind Ens.
Rhythm: Waltz
Tempo: Medium Fast

I SAW THREE SHIPS

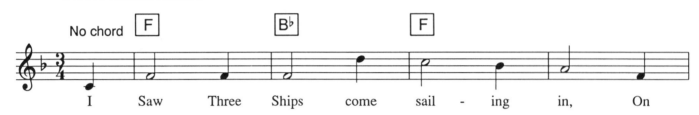

No chord F   B♭   F

I Saw Three Ships come sail - ing in, On

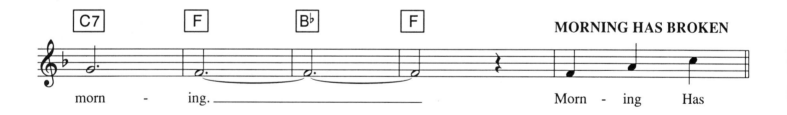

B♭   F   B♭   F

Christ - mas Day, On Christ - mas Day, I Saw Three

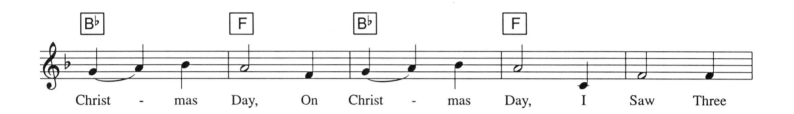

B♭   F   B♭   F

Ships come sail - ing in, On Christ - mas Day in the

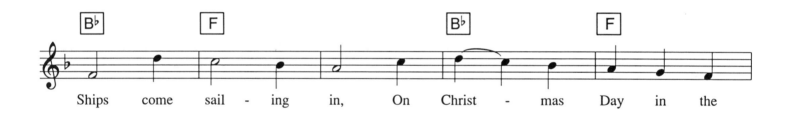

C7   F   B♭   F   **MORNING HAS BROKEN**

morn - ing. _____ Morn - ing Has

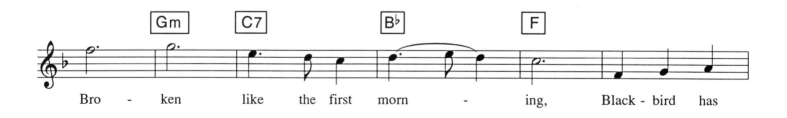

Gm   C7   B♭   F

Bro - ken like the first morn - ing, Black - bird has

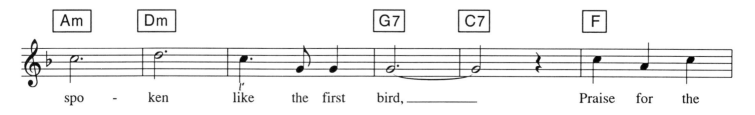

Am   Dm   G7   C7   F

spo - ken like the first bird, _____ Praise for the

42

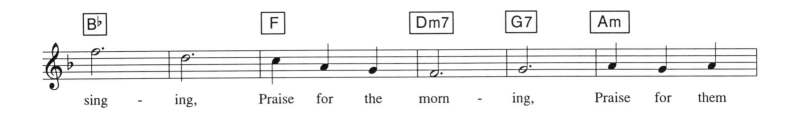

sing - ing,   Praise for the morn - ing,   Praise for them

spring - ing   fresh   from the world. _____

TING-A-LING-A-JINGLE (CHRISTMAS LULLABY)

_   On   the   night be - fore Christ - mas when

San - ta is   near,   All the chil - dren to dream - land will

soon dis - ap - pear; But there's one lit - tle dar - ling that won't close an

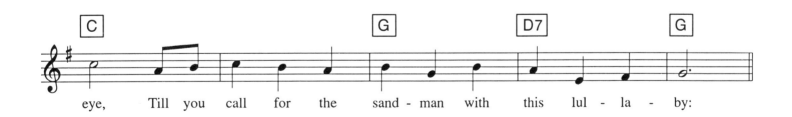

eye,   Till you call for the sand - man with this lul - la - by:

Sing Ting - A - Ling - A Jin - gle and hold me so tight,

HAPPY XMAS (WAR IS OVER)

Medley 12

Registration: Piano or Vibraphone
Rhythm: 6/8 March or Baroque
Tempo: Medium

GOOD CHRISTIAN MEN REJOICE

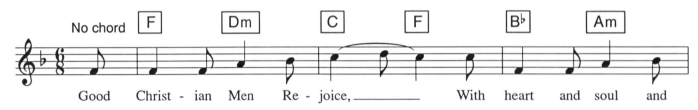

No chord | F | Dm | C | F | B♭ | Am

Good Christ - ian Men Re - joice, _____ With heart and soul and

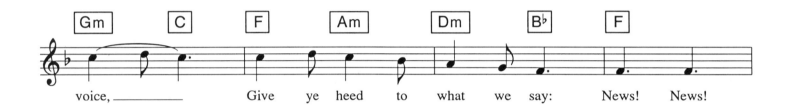

Gm | C | F | Am | Dm | B♭ | F

voice, _____ Give ye heed to what we say: News! News!

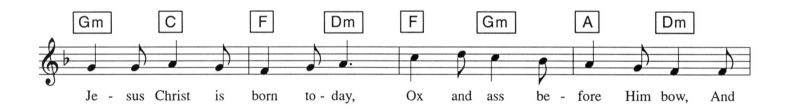

Gm | C | F | Dm | F | Gm | A | Dm

Je - sus Christ is born to - day, Ox and ass be - fore Him bow, And

Gm | C | F | Dm | B♭ | C | Dm | F

He is in the man - ger now, Christ is born to - day, _____

THE GOLDEN CAROL

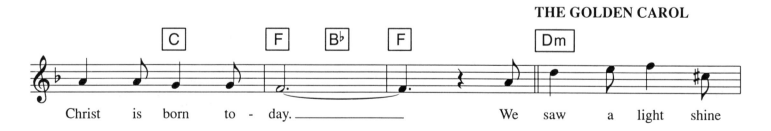

C | F | B♭ | F | Dm

Christ is born to - day. _____ We saw a light shine

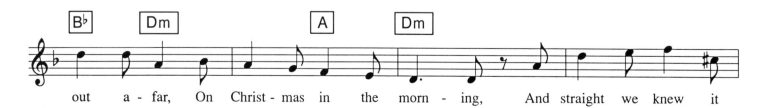

B♭ | Dm | A | Dm

out a - far, On Christ - mas in the morn - ing, And straight we knew it

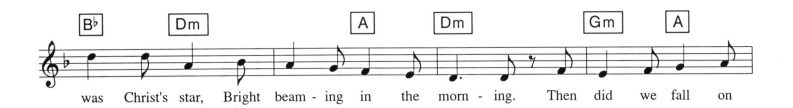

was Christ's star, Bright beam - ing in the morn - ing. Then did we fall on

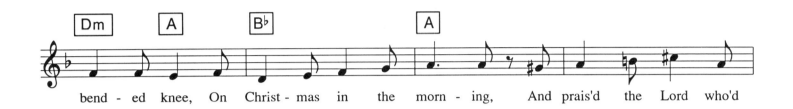

bend - ed knee, On Christ - mas in the morn - ing, And prais'd the Lord who'd

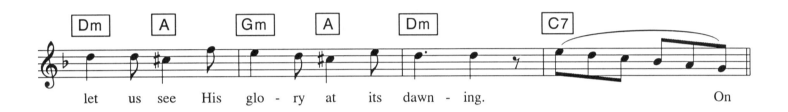

let us see His glo - ry at its dawn - ing. On

ON CHRISTMAS NIGHT ALL CHRISTIANS SING

Christ - mas Night All Christ - ians Sing, To hear the news the an - gels bring, On

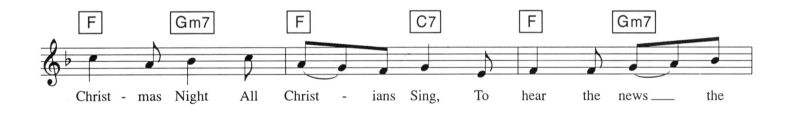

Christ - mas Night All Christ - ians Sing, To hear the news the

an - gels bring, News of great joy, News of great mirth,

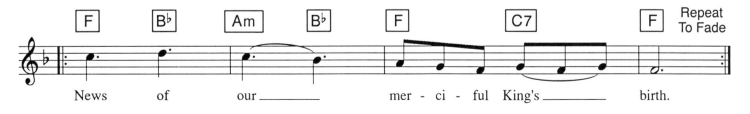

News of our mer - ci - ful King's birth.

The Beatles

Enya

Phil Collins

Van Morrison

Bob Dylan

Sting

Paul Simon

Tracy Chapman

Eric Clapton

Pink Floyd

New Kids On The Block

Bryan Adams

Tina Turner

Elton John

Bee Gees

Whitney Houston

AC/DC

Bringing you the
words

All the latest in rock and pop. Plus the brightest and best in West End show scores. Music books for every instrument under the sun. And exciting new teach-yourself ideas like "Let's Play Keyboard" - in cassette/book packs, or on video. Available from all good music shops.

and
music

Music Sales' complete catalogue lists thousands of titles and is available free from your local music shop, or direct from Music Sales Limited. Please send a cheque or postal order for £1.50 (for postage) to:

Music Sales Limited
Newmarket Road,
Bury St Edmunds,
Suffolk IP33 3YB

Buddy

Five Guys Named Moe

Les Misérables

West Side Story

Phantom Of The Opera

Show Boat

The Rocky Horror Show

**Bringing you the
world's best music.**